Don't Die Ugly

LIVE BEAUTIFULLY

Lynn Soles

Don't Die Ugly

Lynn Soles

2023 © by Lynn Soles

BIBLE SCRIPTURES

🕊 SPIRIT MEDIA

www.spiritmedia.us
1249 Kildaire Farm Rd STE 112
Cary, NC 27511
1 (888) 800-3744

Kindle eBooks | Religion & Spirituality |
Christian Books & Bibles

eBook ISBN: 978-1-961614-65-9
Paperback ISBN: 978-1-961614-64-2
Hardback ISBN: 978-1-961614-66-6
Audiobook ISBN: 978-1-961614-67-3
Library of Congress Control Number: 2023917556

TABLE OF CONTENTS

01

02

03

People Can Be So Ignorant. (No Words)

04

Cancer Friends

05

Feeling Like Job 47

06

Keeping the House Up 57

07

The Positive Value of Learning a New Way of Life 61

08

09

Dedication

I want to dedicate this book to the many people who have been my treatment and support team throughout my journey:

- Bilal Khalid, MD, my oncologist

- Katie Brummer, BSN, RN, my oncology nurse navigator

- My oncology infusion nurses at WakeMed Cancer Care

- Robert Nunoo, MD, FACS, my surgeon

- Samantha "Sam" Adams, BSN, RN, my surgical nurse navigator

- Rendon Nelson, MD, my radiologist

- Our church, Generation Church in Clayton, NC

- My husband's colleagues at Atlanta Flooring and True Homes

And above all, I dedicate this book to my husband, Chris—the love of my life, my partner and encourager to the end, and a remarkably good beauty professional considering that his career is in construction! Chris, I could not do this life without you.

Preface

Try to imagine writing a book about the hardest experience of your life … while you're in the middle of it.

That's what I'm trying to do here. I was diagnosed with colon cancer on Oct. 7, 2022, and I started writing this book on June 13, 2023. When I started writing, I'd been through three months of chemo and 22 days of radiation therapy. I'd had a stent put in my liver because my bile was backing up, and I was getting ready for the second surgery to repair my broken shoulder. I'd only drafted a few chapters when I got the news I would need to have a colostomy.

Until Oct. 7, 2022 I was a young, healthy, and beautiful woman.

After Oct. 7, I began having to work much harder to think I was that woman. But if I didn't want to "die ugly," the way so many cancer patients do, I was going to have to go through some stuff I didn't want to experience.

In July, when they told me I had to have the colostomy, I stopped being able to think that way. Suddenly, I felt old.

And still, I wanted to live. Even if my new "beautiful" would include wearing an ostomy bag.

This book is part journal—including the messy and difficult parts—part encouragement, and part helpful tips for you or anyone you love who faces these challenges. My life has always been about creating beauty, and I want to create beauty with you, even in these difficult moments. Thank you for bringing me with you on your life journey!

Charm is deceptive, and beauty does not last; but a woman who fears the LORD will be greatly praised.

Prov. 31:30 (NLT)

FACING THE GREAT DIVIDE

Maybe it's not a big surprise that my career has been all about beauty. I grew up your classic ugly duckling. I was the last of seven kids, short, scrawny, with glasses. Even into my teens, I looked like I was about twelve years old.

Mom always lets me pick out my own clothing, so I have a second-grade school picture where I'm wearing cat-eye glasses with diamonds on the frames and a blue smocked dress. My hair is in a pixie cut, sticking out all around. That year, we had just moved to Raleigh from a town in New York, and kids at school would make fun of me, saying,

"Where is New York? It must be a different country!" Or even, "Do you get free lunches? We can tell by your outfit!" One of my sisters kept that picture in her wallet for years as a reminder to pray for me. She told me, "You just looked so pitiful that I would pray for you when I saw the picture."

The pixie cut wasn't my idea, though. Shortly before we moved, I'd gotten the chance to stay overnight at my aunt Sandy's. I wanted to be just like her. She was in cosmetology school, and she was gorgeous! She said nobody in North Carolina has long hair because it's hot there. So she cut my hair. She didn't ask anybody, she just cut it.

That was okay with me because I wanted to be like Aunt Sandy. But when I got home, everybody in my house was furious. Of course, since I was just a kid I thought they were angry with me. But there was no going back. I started growing my hair from that day.

Making Myself Beautiful

I got my first job when I was fourteen just so I could replace those glasses with contacts. I worked part-time as a hostess at Darryl's 1840 Restaurant and Tavern in Raleigh. Darryl's had kind of a sports theme, and all the players came there. I'll tell you, as a 4-foot-11 high school freshman, I felt really short when the basketball team came in!

It took me just a couple months to save up enough, and then I went to the optometrist to replace my glasses with contact lenses. Back then, there were no soft contacts, so I had to get hard lenses. They felt like grit in your eyes, and you had to build up calluses on the inside of your eyelids so they weren't quite as uncomfortable. But I was determined to wear them, come hell or high water.

That was when my transformation began. I ran a bit, trying to be physically fit. I got on the aerobics bandwagon, with legwarmers and all. I even taught a few exercise classes. I kept on growing my hair, and had some extensions put in to make it more thick and dramatic. It was down to the middle of my back when I finished high school, and before I started cancer treatment I'd managed to grow it all the way to my waist. That, for me, was a big problem with radiation and chemo. I really worked hard for twenty years to grow that beautiful mane, and now I would lose so much to cancer.

I did wear hand-me-downs back then because I had five older sisters and I inherited their outgrown clothes. But one of my sisters had a boyfriend whose mom was a seamstress. She would revamp a lot of wardrobe for me so things looked completely new. I remember how she took one pair of my sister's bell bottoms, creased the legs and put buttons on along the overlaps. She made them not just up-to-date but unique. People would ask me, "Where'd you get those pants?"

Around that time, I also started playing with makeup. The same lady who revamped my clothes liked to watch soap operas, and I'd look at all the actresses to figure out how they did their faces. I paid the most attention to the ones I thought were artistic and very good with their makeup. Then I'd try things at home. I did a lot of contouring, because I have a big Italian nose that was very prominent at that time because I was still so little. I contoured my cheekbones. I practiced smoky eyes and heavy eyeliners. I worked out how to draw attention away from my big teeth—in my family, we have really big teeth, like rabbits! And I didn't share my secrets with anyone.

As I learned about beauty and could apply makeup, I felt so much better about myself and that became an important part of my life. It gave me some confidence socially. Because I was so artistic, in high school I did all the set designs for plays and special events like homecoming and prom. But I was pretty sheltered—a good Catholic girl—so I didn't go out on dates. I just stayed home and drew pictures. When my own prom came, my brother-in-law took me. I wore the dress I'd worn in their wedding and he wore a white tux with cowboy boots and his big mustache. It was funny to watch everyone respond!

That new self-confidence also showed up in my art work, which was starting to get a bit more creative. I started entering shows, showing at different galleries. I was recognized with a Scholastic Presidential Gold Key award and got art scholarships to go to college at Eastern Carolina University. I was planning to earn a degree in commercial art there, but I came home and finished at the community college near where Mom lived in Clayton. My plan was to do advertising art and be a book illustrator ... I would have loved to become a Disney illustrator!

Creating Artistic Beauty

Things turned out a bit different, as they usually do, but my focus stayed on using my artistic skills to create beauty. I found myself doing commissioned murals all over Eastern North Carolina, as towns and cities looked for ways to add beauty to their business districts. I started teaching private art classes.

In studio instruction, I quickly discovered that I was teaching more than how to make a beautiful work of art. I was helping people discover how they could create their own beautiful lives. People would come to me with a particular goal for their artwork, and I would show them step by step on to reach that goal. But as we were talking, I would be asking them what other goals they have for their lives. And step by step, we'd work out how they would get there.

Sometimes the goals are about art. I've had students become art teachers, do their own art shows, learn to sell their art and market it. Sometimes, there are other goals. But it's always a step-by-step process to reach them. And as people get used to planning steps and going through them, they apply it to all of their lives. That's one-way art becomes like therapy for them.

Creating Women's Personal Beauty

Since I've always enjoyed making myself beautiful with makeup, it might not surprise you that I landed in a career that helps other women look beautiful. One of the things I love to do is professional makeup for people who are having professional photos and videos shot. A lot of what I do now is permanent makeup. I'll do their eyebrows or their lips, maybe they want permanent eyeliner or eyeshadow. Some people say, "How vain is it to tattoo your makeup on?" I think it's less vain than checking your makeup in the mirror several times a day to make sure your eyebrows are still symmetrical and your lips aren't sweating off!

But I didn't get into this because I was worried about vanity. What motivated me was the first permanent makeup job I ever received.

Right after I finished high school, I designed a tattoo for my sister and I went to the studio with her to supervise its application. I saw someone there tattooing lips, and the idea that I could stop putting on lipstick and contouring around my mouth seemed really appealing. I decided I wanted to have permanent lipstick myself.

I was able to have it done right then! And it turned out really bad. I looked like Lucille Ball. It was very embarrassing. For years, I had to work hard every day to cover up those bright red lips with lipliner and lipstick.

Doing permanent makeup lets me help people who are in medical treatment. One cancer patient asked me, "Can we please do my brows before I lose my hair?" I helped one woman who had been beaten to get her own face back. Her surgeons had reconstructed her face but she still had deep scars and no eyebrows. When I was done, she looked in the mirror and started to cry. "I look like a normal person!" she said. I do a lot of areola reconstruction for women who have had mastectomies. That comes by referrals from their surgeons, too.

But I kept on doing tattoo design. As an artist, what I do is design the transfer that a tattoo artist will apply to your body to guide their work. People like to have something original tattooed instead of just getting flash art, where they look in a book and pick something out. That's kind of like clip art for your body, and some people really want something different. I became accomplished at tattooing myself. Sometimes people who already have some flash art call on me to create a new design that connects their existing tattoos into a larger theme. That takes a lot of creativity! You have to be able to see what's there and see how you can make it something else.

I decided I had to learn how to do permanent makeup so I could fix those terrible lips. And to this day, I do all my own permanent makeup. I'm more confident in myself than anyone else. I began doing permanent makeup more than twenty years ago. I opened my first clinic in 2000. I worked hard juggling a lot of hats to pay for art school and then my permanent beauty training; now my permanent makeup business floats my art business. I do a lot of portraits, and I discovered that I loved to draw people. Then I discovered that I loved to draw on people. And that's what I mostly do now.

I see five to six clients a day. Some of them are people recovering from surgery, and I take time to really listen to what their goals are before we start anything. I do scar revisions where people have facial skin cancers removed. Women with breast cancer, I can restore their areolas. I work with plastic surgeons to help them with scar revisions.

Then there are the people who want eyeliner done, eyelash enhancement, or brows. They can be any age, and men also come to me for things like eyelashes and tattoos. Brows are big. I fix a lot of permanent makeup that was done by someone who was just learning—maybe their granddaughter who was learning how to do this. Things can be hard to fix, and there's a lot of responsibility and risk. Old tattoo ink can migrate even if it's been there for twenty years. Correction work reminds me of bad decisions in life … permanent reminders of something you shouldn't have done. I am working on a canvas begun by someone other than myself. I have to think about what inks might have been used, and how they would heal in the skin overtime. It's much planning to "fix" someone else's work. I become responsible for it. But I'm really good at what I do. I often hear, "Can you do my brows before I begin chemotherapy? Before they fall out." I spend an hour and a half with someone and change their appearance for the better. People look in the mirror afterward, and they cry! It's so rewarding.

I would give anything to be at work right now, helping someone else overcome her challenges! Work is one of my happy places, where creativity and client relationships happen. When I'm doing my work I'm not focused on me. My business has two exam rooms, a lobby and an art room at the back. That way, if there's a little time, I can work on my art or teach art lessons.

Part of my work now is doing production makeup for men and women before they have their professional photos and videos shot. I call this service "Put Your Best Face Forward," and it really empowers people to feel more positive about themselves. This isn't glamor or wedding makeup, but the kind of makeup that helps a dignitary or public speaker photograph well. It makes the person who's getting photographed feel more confident knowing that nothing is sticking out the wrong way and if the camera is getting a profile view, it will still look great.

Oct. 7, 2022: The great divide

The day I got the cancer diagnosis divided my life into before and after. Until Oct. 7, 2022, my life had been about my business, creating beauty, staying fit—everything I thought I could control. Then all of a sudden I didn't have any of that. My life would be totally different from then on. I would have scars I'd never had before; a lifestyle I'd never known before. I had a life that I couldn't control anymore. I entered a huge period of mourning my loss of what was, and I was going on to whatever it would be without even knowing what it would be. My "what will be" would keep changing. That's really hard for me. I'm the kind of person that if you give me a mark, I'll shoot for it. But cancer would keep moving the mark.

I came home from the doctor's office, told my husband, and we just held each other and cried for a long time. Then we determined that we would do this—whatever "this" is—together. Forever.

I didn't want to have chemo and radiation because I had never seen that work in a way that I wanted to live through. I thought there would be an alternative. Something holistic and not harming my body. Everyone is always worse off, I thought. I didn't want all those visits with the surgeon and the oncologist. I wanted to do nothing. I wanted to drink organic tea …

But the doctors said cancer isn't a pretty way to die. So … My journey began.

A lot of people wonder why it matters to me to maintain a graceful appearance while I'm in cancer treatment. It's partly because I don't want people to ask me all the time, "Are you okay? You don't look so good." I don't want to have to respond to all the weird things people say when they think someone is sick. I'm not brave, and I don't want to hear people say "You got this" when I'm not at all sure I do!

But I know I'm not alone in this struggle. There are more than 750,000 women each year in the US are diagnosed with cancers. More than 150,000 men and women are diagnosed each year with the kind of cancer I have. Every one of those patients needs a community of care around them, and every one of them needs the people around them to help them see "the future and the hope" that God has for them, even while they're being treated. This was the loneliest time for me… because I couldn't let anyone into this distress. I want others to know God knows. God is there. God sees. God has given each of us our own beautiful place in the beautiful world He created.

That's why I'm still working to create beauty. Even with cancer and an unpredictable future, I can live beautifully on the inside. I can speak honestly, live with dignity and courage, and accept the things that come with grace. Nobody can feel sorry for a woman who lives with that kind of beauty.

I hope you'll find your own path to beauty as you read this book.

LIVING WITH CHEMO BRAIN

On Monday, Oct. 10, just three days after my diagnosis, my husband Chris and I met with an oncologist and a surgeon. I had seen people go through cancer treatment, and it wasn't pretty. So I told them I wouldn't accept any treatment. I still thought I might be able to beat this without intervention. You know, drink tea …

Oct. 10, 2022 'Don't Die Ugly'

They disagreed in the strongest terms. "Cancer isn't a pretty way to die," they told me. "You don't want to die ugly."

The first step in the treatment they proposed was chemotherapy. The specific treatment for this kind of cancer is called FolFox, which sounds to me like something from Mission: Impossible. It's a chemo cocktail of three different drugs that kills cancer cells and keeps them from spreading. I would be part of a family of cancer survivors ... who accepted the challenge and made it! But FolFox also kills healthy cells that multiply quickly, like skin cells, the cells in the GI tract, and hair follicles. That's why patients in chemotherapy often lose their hair.

I protested that Chris and I had already booked our anniversary trip to Aruba. We were scheduled to fly out that Saturday! I couldn't possibly start chemo. Besides, I really think I'm supposed to live there ...

"Go to Aruba," the doctor said. "Have way too much fun. We'll start this after." Mission accepted! Sun and fun, here I come! I jumped off a boat to snorkel in the ocean, I caught the biggest triggerfish, which we ate right there on the beach! We went on my first "party boat," we took a glass bottom kayak in their beautiful ocean, and I had way too much fun as the doctor ordered.

Oct. 31, 2022 Chemo begins

We got back from Aruba on Oct. 22, a Saturday, and on Monday Oct. 31 the doctor installed a port right under my right collarbone. That port is what they would use to infuse the chemo cocktail into my bloodstream. Where the port is, I'm still a bit swollen and it looks like a bruise. It connects with a major vein in my neck. Looks a little robotic. I was booked for eight infusion treatments of three days each, to be given on alternate weeks at the infusion center at WakeMed's main hospital in Raleigh. That meant I'd be in chemotherapy until the middle of February.

I was determined to keep things as normal as I could. In the weeks I was treated, I worked Monday and Tuesday, then was infused on Wednesday morning at WakeMed for four to five hours. I'd wear a different chemo bag home, and that drug went into me on Thursday and Friday mornings. Then I'd take it off and clean the port, and sometimes I'd go to work at my office on Friday evening.

But cancer treatment has a way of overturning your normal. One of the ways it hit me was what people call "chemo brain."

Chemo Takes Over My Brain

"Chemo brain" sounds like something people would make up. Like "Mom brain," right? It's so weird how foggy your mind can get in the days and weeks after you've given birth, but it's just a thing that mothers know about and get each other through.

Except now science knows that "Mom brain" is real. It's a casual term, but it describes the way real brain changes after giving birth affect a Mom's ability to do her everyday life.

"Chemo brain" is also a real thing. It's not just in your head. The Mayo Clinic describes it on their website as "thinking and memory problems that can occur during and after cancer treatment." If you want to sound more technical, you could say it's a cancer-related cognitive impairment involving loss of focus and concentration. Not ideal for the control freak …

For me, it came as a foggy sensation in my memory. It became difficult to concentrate my thoughts. You can misplace items you just had in your hand, and you think you're going crazy! I was reminded of my mom losing stuff and making me look for it. Sometimes I'd lose the word for something, almost like a person who's had a stroke. I remember one time I wanted to say something about the tomatoes from our garden and I could not get the word "tomatoes" out of my mouth. I would just name things by their color until the right word would come to mind. So "tomatoes" became "red." And in my artwork I concentrated on colors and what happens when they mix. I would be captivated by Chris's paint pours, watching the colors twirl and cell. I could get all creative and then forget what I wanted to do.

A study at the University of Sydney found that bowel cancers like mine can cause memory loss even before you get your diagnosis. Great, right? They didn't figure out why it happens; they just found that we're three times more likely to have memory problems than other people, with or without chemotherapy. Here's my take on that: when your bowels are messed up, you have to pay a lot of attention to them and it becomes a major part of your day. So your mind is fixated on that instead of being able to focus on other things. What did I just eat? How will that pass? These are things you just don't talk about. We went to the movies once when I was all cramped up, and I don't even remember what was playing.

Me being a multitasker by nature, my chemo brain has been a real challenge. I'm used to focusing on more than one thing, but my chemo brain jumps from one thought to another as if I had ADD (attention-deficit disorder). And my multitasker's attempt to compensate was to jump even more from thought to thought as I tried to make sure I didn't lose track of anything. Let me tell you: That doesn't work.

When you're trying to look at so many things at one time without being able to focus, you're not seeing the big picture. Like consequences. You don't look ahead to the consequences. That's one of the reasons I fell off a ladder. More about that later.

Managing Life with Chemo Brain

Happily, chemo brain does go away gradually over time. But while you're dealing with it, there are ways to better manage chemo brain. Here are some that work for me and for other people:

- **Make lists.** My husband has lived his whole life making lists. I never had to, so he taught me this. The good thing about making a list is you won't have to worry you'll forget something, because once it's on the list, you can focus on whatever else you're doing. Some things you might not think of listing are: What did I eat for dinner? What shirt did I wear last week that I thought I rocked? Who can I call for a ride to the dentist?

- **Sticky notes are great.** They make it easy to put your reminders where you'll see them exactly when you need them. I'd put them on the bathroom door to remind me to take a particular medicine. Some people put them on the coffee maker to remind them what they need to do first in the morning. A sticky note on your steering wheel is great … keep them handy in the car to remind you of something you need to accomplish.

- **Use a real, physical calendar,** one that's not on your phone. When your routines have been changed so much, you can forget what day it is. I need a calendar to remember it's Tuesday today! I put doctor's appointments on it, birthdays, everything, and it works much better for me than Google calendar. My paper calendar helps me to see a big picture of time and recognize things like, "That's a radiation week. It will be busy." I carry my calendar with me so I can look at it. And at the end of the week, I synch it with a work calendar to make sure I've contacted clients and such.

- **Take breaks to rest.** Chemo is making it harder for your brain to do its job, so make sure you give yourself enough rest. In my case, I started to add a few minutes between clients at work so I could take a quick break.

- **Reduce stress any way you can.** Stress adds to memory problems. Over time, I had to learn that I just couldn't do all the things I did before. So I had to stop stressing over things that would have to wait, like cleaning the dust from under the bedroom bureau. Even the "drama" of relationship ups and downs had to be taken down a notch. Maybe I can't meet a friend for coffee or lunch ... I read a story of a lady going through cancer treatment watching ladies share a salad on an outside restaurant porch. "Who has time for salads!" she said to herself. Well, I don't right now ... but in the future, when I can manage friendships again, I may have time for salads.

- **Exercise whatever ways you can.** During a lot of chemo, just getting out of bed is hard, so don't push yourself when what you need is rest! But when you are able to move around, a change of scenery might do you good, and the movement itself might feel good. I really like the "wall" exercises that help my core. And no special equipment needed. I found them in the Google rabbit hole.

- **Organize your time according to your energy.** There will be times of day or days of the week when you have more energy and others when all you want to do is sleep. Schedule yourself so you can do what's most important to you when you have enough energy for it. Then when you're ready, organizing your space can clear your head.

- **Control your surroundings as best you can.** For me, cluttered surroundings leave me feeling cluttered and dirty inside, so I learned to rely on helpers to keep up with what was too much for me. Accept the blessing of someone doing your dishes for you, even if your kitchen doesn't look like it came from the Magnolia Network. Which leads to ...

- **Enlist helpers.** Friends and family can help keep track of things that need to be done. I'm really blessed that my husband, Chris, comes to my medical appointments with me so I don't have to worry about forgetting something I want to tell the doctor or something the doctor told me.

I'm sure you'll find other things that work for you, too. You'll probably also discover that part of what works is allowing yourself to do the best you can now, not what was your best before. Chemo is always hard, but it's also essential. I didn't believe that before, but I'm understanding it now. "Give us a year" the doctors said. "We can fix this." I'm not going to tell you "You got this!" because that's one of the worst things people say to me. In fact, in the next chapter, I'm going to tell you a bunch of the terrible things you might hear from people who just don't know what to say.

*Rejoice with those who rejoice;
mourn with those who mourn.*

Rom. 12:15 (NIV)

PEOPLE CAN BE SO IGNORANT.
(NO WORDS)

Cancer has changed my life so much. I lost a ton of weight, which I'm slowly gaining back. I was a physically fit person before this. I ran, I had nice arms. It's been depressing to see loose skin where there used to be muscle. I was running two profitable businesses, then I had to keep moving clients around because of my treatments. I even had to close a couple of months, which was a challenge financially. The bills don't stop because you're sick. The landlord may feel bad for you, but the world keeps revolving even when you're not.

Why Work Matters

Work matters to me even while I'm in treatment because it keeps my mind occupied with things other than cancer. It makes it easier to push off even thinking about the next treatment until that very day. It helps me focus on another person, their needs and care.

I meet my clients in a professional atmosphere. Women are used to confiding in beauty personnel, and they confide in me. What's the latest hurdle they have faced? How are their kids? Is there a job situation that needs prayer, a spouse with a newfound diagnosis? A new grandchild? A marriage? These are important conversations. I can't give them words that will guide them, but I can listen, look them in the eye, and try to feel their feelings. That's in line with my personality, and it's also in line with what the Bible says:

Be happy with those who are happy, and weep with those who weep. Rom. 12:15 NLT

What's harder right now is that my clients expect reciprocation. They share their lives with me, and they expect me to share my life with them. That's what I've always done. But right now, there's a lot I don't want to talk about. I don't want to scare them! I don't want them to think I can't take care of them. Of course, the ones I do share with often become some of my best pray-ers.

Appearances matter in my job, and keeping my appearance up is part of how I appear competent to my clients. So the girl who always did my hair bought me a few wigs, and cut them to look like my own hair. When my eyelashes fell out, my husband would do my eyelashes for me.

When I first got diagnosed, I sent out mass emails to all my clients, assuring them that I was confident I could take care of them. I didn't want to make everything about me and my sickness. I wanted to be upbeat, tell of future plans. I am always looking for things to look forward to.

But there have been times when the sickness has taken control. It felt terrible when I was trying to run my business with endless cancellations for treatments. Financially, it was a mess, and I just missed my career and the relationships that are part of it.

Terrible Things to Tell a Cancer Patient

People often are startled to hear about a cancer diagnosis. A lot of people are afraid of cancer, even though so many treatments are successful.

Because of their fear, many people say things that aren't very helpful. And while I generally keep my response to myself, I've got to admit that what I'd like to say sometimes is pretty rude!

- "Oh my God, Lynn! Do you think you'll die?" one woman asked me. I shut that woman down, but it haunted me. Why in the world would she say that to me? Did her mama not teach her manners?

- "Girl, you got this" I wanted to smack anyone who said this. I don't "got this" I've got cancer, and you're just glad it's not you. I remember thinking this when someone was going through something stressful … "I'm glad it's you and not me." Please never utter these four words aloud to anyone … Ever.

- Frivolous prayer requests can be more than a little irritating. One day, a lady said to some of us on social media, "Please pray for me y'all, I've gotta get this tooth worked on and I'd rather have my three children naturally again than go through this." My first reaction can't be printed. I wanted her to shut up and stop making such a huge issue out of such a small thing. The world won't stop if your mouth is sore for a week.

- "Well my goodness, see how much better you're doing!" one of the other ladies getting chemo said to me one day. No, I'm not doing better, I thought. I just have wigs and permanent makeup that make me look better. Give me a break! Don't they know I threw up just before I saw them?

- "You need to … You should …" No, I don't! And maybe I shouldn't! Every person with cancer is a different person. What was right for someone else—or what you imagine would be good for someone—might not be good for me now. Because I'm sick doesn't mean you can fix me.

- "My mom had colon cancer and she died." Why would anyone think that is appropriate? I get that my cancer is reminding her of how cancer ripped her mother out of her life. Will it help to remind me that cancer can kill?

- Spiritual "wisdom" can be a problem. I believe that God heals people; I also know that God decides who to heal and when. Telling me "God promised your healing in the Word, so maybe you're not choosing to be healed" is a slap in my face. You're blaming me for my suffering instead of doing anything that would be helpful.

Sometimes I've felt embarrassed to answer when people ask how I'm doing because I know they've been praying for me and I don't want to tell them that God wasn't moving the way they'd asked for. I remember my mother telling me that you don't have to defend the Holy Spirit; the Holy Spirit can take care of Himself. But I felt like I was letting them down if I didn't have good news. I don't want to give people a sad update. I didn't want to be that person who hogs prayer channels at church … But pray some more saints, cause this ain't over yet!

I've been grateful for the friends and clients who would just listen. Those are the people who let me look them in the eye and tell them that I was mad or struggling, and they wouldn't try to give me advice or placate me. Just listening makes such a big difference.

It might be surprising, but even doctors don't always know a good way to talk with a patient. So the day I had the colonoscopy that led to my diagnosis, the doctor broke the news to me like this:

"Do you have children or brothers and sisters? Because you have cancer and it's genetic."

Try to imagine: I was just coming out of anesthesia, I was expecting to wake up and go home, and that's the first word out of the doctor's mouth! All I wanted to do was see my mom and go home. I couldn't process this.

I was told of a woman whose son had died. She quit going out places because she would get so angry with people who acted as if they knew how she felt. Or would offer platitudes. She began to dislike people in general. So sad.

Of course, stupid remarks aren't limited to the ill-at-ease friends of cancer patients. In the chapter about Cancer Friends, we'll talk about some of the more helpful ways to respond to your friends with cancer or other big life challenges.

Cancer Myths That Just Aren't True!

It's easier to be a good friend when you know the truth instead of being stuck in cancer myths. So here are some things people think about cancer that just aren't true. And I believed some of these before I knew the truth.

- **Myth:** You can catch cancer.

  Truth: 95 percent of cancers are just cell mutations that develop through your lifetime. It's not contagious. So you don't need to be afraid of your friend who has cancer. You won't catch it.

- **Myth:** You can get cancer from antiperspirants.

  Truth: Antiperspirant roll-on deodorants do not cause cancer, according to the National Cancer Institute. But you can get cancer from tobacco (smoking, chewing, and second-hand smoke), some foods, and many toxic chemicals people are mostly exposed to on the job, some viruses, and even alcoholic beverages.

- **Myth:** You can cure cancer at home with these products!

  Truth: No herbal product scientifically can cure cancer. Many can help you cope with side effects, but others can really interfere with how your chemo and radiation work. So someone recommended noni juice to me, and that's one my doctor says can interfere. Bottom line: Your doctors don't want you taking something that will affect your blood sugars or other things they measure because that might affect their assessment of your medical tests.

- **Myth:** A positive attitude improves your odds of beating cancer.

  Truth: No scientific evidence that says if you have a positive attitude you'll have a better outcome for your treatment. Everyone says to just be positive, but that's not true. It can make things worse because you don't feel comfortable telling people about sadness, anger, or how discouraged you are. A person with cancer shouldn't have to hide her fears or her tears.

Don't Offer Snake Oil and Miracle Drugs!

Every week, a well-meaning friend or colleague comes to me with a recommendation for some "snake oil" or miracle drugs. They start out by asking, "Have you tried [this supplement, that mineral, this diet, these pills, this all-natural tea]? It cured my grandpa of Stage 4 lung cancer!" Then they say, "And you can get them for way less when you become a distributor! Please, I'm leaving you with a pamphlet to read. It's way better than chemo and radiation … the pharmaceutical companies just don't want you to know…"

When my daughter, Meghan, was diagnosed with lupus, the miracle concoction gods came calling. I was mad about it then, and I still get hot under the collar now.

No, no, no! Do not go to a sick person with snake oil ever!

I took one of those supplements to my oncologist and asked what she thought. "A good friend gave this to me. Is it okay if I take it?" I asked.

"Hmm," she said. "We have noni trees where I grew up, and we never thought about eating them." We had a big laugh. Then she suggested, "While you're under treatment, just tell your friends and colleagues we don't want you taking any supplements now."

Most of these offers were just a multilevel marketing thing, so I was glad she gave me words to close the door. I know these were well-meaning clients, colleagues, and friends, but no one should go to a sick person with an offer of snake oil. Ever! And it's just offensive when the offer of help also means "and let me hook you into my business."

Now I did get one offer that was actually worth something.

Nov. 5, 2022 The Miracle Drug That Worked!

The weekend after I started chemo, I was so sick. I got to thinking that I couldn't go through a year of nausea and pain. I started thinking that maybe like my friend, Marcie, I should just enjoy what I can and let the cancer run its course.

One of my husband's friends was over that weekend. He thought what had been helping him might help me. So a couple weeks later, he brought me some THC edibles.

In case you don't know, THC comes from marijuana, and some people swear by it for pain, nausea, and anxiety. It's also illegal in the state where I live.

"Will you try this?" he asked.

"I will not!!" I said. I mean, I'm a teetotaler! No way I'm taking an illegal drug.

But I felt so sick. So I asked my pharmacist.

Well, she can't recommend anything that's illegal, of course. "I can't tell you about that," she said with a smile. "But you need to think outside the box."

So I tried them, and that was the only thing that got me through the nausea and pain. I didn't take it when I worked, and I didn't take too much of it, but those second and third days after a chemo infusion were the toughest, and they really worked for me. The doctors gave me a lot of pills, but THC is what worked. I ended up throwing much of the nausea meds away. For me, that was a game-changer. And totally outside the box. I'm just so sorry that it is not made available to patients who really need this natural painkiller.

Because I tried them, I don't want to judge other people for trying things. I'd just quote my pharmacist: Think outside the box.

The Holidays

When Thanksgiving rolled around, I couldn't believe how tired I was. I've always been the one who hosted holidays, and this year I had a very different role. On Thanksgiving, instead of me preparing the big meal, my mother-in-law brought over a ham and chicken breasts. Chris made his awesome Seven-Layer Cake. My sister came for dessert, because no one wants to miss that cake! My daughter, Meghan, and her kids came for a short time, and that was very sweet. But I had to run away and go upstairs because I was so tired.

Christmas was also very low-key. Meghan and her husband came over in the afternoon with the grandkids; our son Dillon and his girlfriend Lindsay, too. I'm not really sure what we ate, but I know I didn't cook it.

There were endless tears during those early-to-bed months. I was still trying to work full-time but as I grew weaker physically, there was a darkness coming over my mind.

I'd finished all my chemo and radiation long before the Fourth of July rolled around, but I still wasn't ready to be the kind of host I usually am. Most years, I'd have done two or three days of prep for a big all-day family party … not this year! My daughter and the grandkids came by around six in the evening; we grilled some chicken and salmon and shrimp on the barbeque, then went to watch the fireworks from a big store parking lot. That is probably the best I had felt in so long.

February 2023 I Had a Great Fall

I mentioned before that I had fallen off a ladder. Here's how that happened. I had just driven home from work, and I could not find my keys to get into the house. What was I going to do? I looked up at the house in frustration, then remembered: My husband had gone in through a window in the downstairs bathroom one time when we lost our keys. I thought, "I'm littler than he is. I can do this!" So I got the ladder out and started climbing.

That was my "chemo brain" thinking for me. Usually, I would have known better than to go up a ladder with no one to hold it steady. But "chemo brain" loses track of a lot of important things. You can lose the word for something you want to say, almost like a stroke victim. In this moment, I lost track of the potential consequences. I didn't even call Chris first to see where he was. I just got to the top of that ladder and tried to open the window.

I fell … hard … broke both shoulders at the same time. I felt like Humpty Dumpty. I knew in that instant that I just made a huge setback for myself. The orthopedic doctor was sympathetic. He said, "When you walked in here, I didn't expect to see this on your X-ray. It's going to be dreadful for you, but we have to fix them at the same time. There's no other choice." I had to have surgery. Forget work or doing anything independently for a good while!

You can't do anything with no arms! Imagine a little Italian T-Rex: that was me. My mom-in-law and Chris took care of me … feeding me … dressing me … brushing my teeth. They put me in the car like a baby, buckling me up because I couldn't do it. Physical therapists would come to my home because I couldn't drive. You should see the scars! I mourned my previously fit arms. Now they were puny and sagging.

I had to take two months off while they started to heal. My clients are great, and they waited for me to get back. Working was uncomfortable, but not terrible, I was just so glad to be working again. Then they X-rayed me to make sure everything was okay ... and it wasn't. My right shoulder was out of whack. The humerus bone wasn't in the rotator cuff where it belonged. I didn't find it humorous in the least! I had a grand meltdown over it. Chris let me cry uncontrollably for about five minutes and then sternly told me to get over it. We could do this, he said. We could help me get better ... together ... forever. I'm a blessed woman.

I scheduled the shoulder surgery. I tried to reschedule a radiation appointment earlier in the day that I was going to have the procedure. My radiologist called me and said, "What are you thinking? No you can't have surgery right now... not till after radiation." So he called my orthopedic doctor and made another surgery appointment for when radiation was done. Of course, the doctor insisted I had to take more time off from work. I needed to be a really good patient, or I wouldn't have a shoulder.

That really hurt. I love what I do, and that shoulder was really affecting my business, which is part of who I am. I honestly couldn't believe my "bad luck" and began wondering who the heck I could have offended in a past life ... and I don't even believe in reincarnation! Go figure.

I give the reader permission to laugh at me, because if I was watching this play out in a movie, I'd have a belly laugh myself.

The Absolute Worst Thing Anyone Ever Said to Me

One day, a professional colleague called asking how I was doing. She asked a lot of questions, and it seemed like she was really listening. That felt so good, that someone who knew me just from work would take that much time!

So I poured out my heart to her. That was when I'd just gotten back to work after my second shoulder surgery, and it was still uncomfortable to move in some of the ways my work requires. I was thankful that it was working out though. I told her about the rollercoaster ups and downs and all I was going through … wait for it … and then she asks me, "Could you teach me to do what you do?"

Wait … what? You didn't call to really bless me and be a friend? You want my job?!

That was like a punch in the gut. I was already concerned about my career and losing my business, and here's a colleague waiting around like a vulture to see when I'm going to drop off, so she can move in on what I built. I got this fleeting feeling that others were just waiting in the wings and they wouldn't be heartbroken at all if I had to close my doors. My mind started running rampant on everything I'd done to build that business, and I felt betrayed. Social media is a helpful tool to stay in touch and let clients in on your life, but let me tell you … be careful airing your pain to everyone out there. If a colleague can sense weakness and try to pounce, that adds even more stress to the process of trying to get better.

Of course, I try to think forward. So I try to focus on the plaque I have hanging in my clinic. "Underestimate me. That'll be fun!" When I bought it, I was thinking about God. It's easy to underestimate God because He can do above and beyond anything we can ask or imagine. I mean, it's not possible to correctly estimate what God can accomplish, and it's fun to see what more He can do!

Now to Him who is able to do exceedingly abundantly above all that we ask or think, according to the power that works in us, to Him be glory in the church by Christ Jesus to all generations, forever and ever. Amen. (Eph. 3:20-21, NKJV)

But now I'm applying that idea to myself. I'm seeing what God can do through me, in my weakness.

But he said to me, "My grace is sufficient for you, for my power is made perfect in weakness." Therefore I will boast all the more gladly about my weaknesses, so that Christ's power may rest on me. That is why, for Christ's sake, I delight in weaknesses, in insults, in hardships, in persecutions, in difficulties. For when I am weak, then I am strong. (2 Cor. 12:9-10, NIV)

All right ya'll. "Hold my beer" … Underestimate me. That'll be fun!

One who has unreliable friends soon comes to ruin, but there is a friend who sticks closer than a brother.

Prov. 18:24 (NIV)

CANCER FRIENDS

Cancer friends aren't an entirely new set of friends, but there's a special kind of friend you really love when you have cancer. You have to put a lot of your life and relationships on hold while you're overwhelmed physically and emotionally by your treatments. You're watching other people's lives continue while yours screeches to a halt. Not everyone understands how to be a friend when you have cancer.

It's hard not to rush the moment when you're visiting a sick friend. You want them to feel better, and you want to offer help. But when I'm in a horrible moment, that's the moment I've been given at that time. If you just smile and tell me, "Girl, you got this!" that's rushing the moment. I actually can't stand that phrase! It's so dishonest, so easy to say, and it sounds so flippant. I have **this** moment; it's a painful

---

and difficult moment; I don't even know what's coming in the next moment. I'm not so brave to be confident that "I got" something as huge and difficult as this. I just need you to stay here at this moment with me.

Or people tell me, "I'll pray for you." I know they're well-meaning and good-hearted. I need prayers and am so thankful that many of those who say this mean it! They actually are taking the time and moment to present me before the Great Physician and plead for me. But then I feel kind of stuck the next time I see them if things aren't going better. I want to be able to give God glory, and if people have latched onto the idea that God will heal me, I want them to see results. Of course, it's God's job to get the results that He is after in my life. And I do see results! I'm thankful for them. They're just not always the results other people are praying for. I want to be a reason that their faith is strengthened, not weakened. Then I begin to think asking for more prayers is making me that "squeaky wheel" I never wanted to be.

When you're visiting a sick friend, you have to learn to deal with that uncomfortable place in you that doesn't want to think about suffering and death. You also have to admit to yourself that there's nothing you can do about what's happening to your friend. I was with my mother, my dad, and my father-in-law when they were dying. It was a lot like having a baby. You can't stop a baby from coming when you're in labor and you can't stop the death process from coming when it's time.

Some people you thought would be there for you when you're sick just aren't. Their lives are busy. Maybe you expected that a particular friend or relative would check in on you more often, or call to pray with you on the phone, or come by to clean your house. You have to remind yourself that of course they care, but they're not the ones you can count on. You have to learn to recognize who "your people" are, and they're not always who you expected they would be.

You also have to learn to ask for what you want, and that's not always part of the relationships you had before cancer. So, for one example, I might want a hug from my grandkids. I'm learning to call my daughter, Meghan, and say, "Can you come by so I can get some hugs?" Maybe you wish that everyone would just naturally think to do what you want them to do, but it doesn't always work out. You try to not take it personally, so you learn to ask.

You'll be surprised how many new friends you discover, too, and how many friendships deepen because you are sharing a challenge.

My Cancer Friend Marcie

One of my clients, a dear friend named Marcie, found out she had throat cancer. She called me and I couldn't understand what she was saying. So I went to visit her in the hospital. She had started chemotherapy, but then she decided to stop because it made her so sick. I did listen and offered what worked for me. She saw her death approaching, and she was angry about it at first. "You always look forward to your golden years," she told me, "and then you get told this." It seems so unfair. Another wave of betrayal washes over us. I just sat with her. Did you know that is where the word "wake" comes from? In Jewish communities when someone was facing death or had passed, just sitting with them is the custom. No words … just presence.

Marcie didn't want to spend the end of her life in a hospice house; she wanted to be out with her family doing things. It was interesting to hear that she was upset that she was dying and still could be satisfied and happy with her plans; she was looking forward to the future and not seeing it as an "end." It was good to hear her being positive about something like going to the beach for the day with her family. Once she let me know how much she appreciated the way her permanent makeup helped her look good when she goes out, I loaned her some wigs, too. I had a few that were shorter, and I cut one of them for her, and of course she could also cut it how she likes it. It's always been important to me even when I feel bad not to look bad, so I understand that. As a cancer friend, you look out for clues like these. It gives you a way to be there. Keep your radar up, dear reader!

The Love of My Life

My husband Chris has been my best friend for as long as I've known him, and my cancer has only brought us closer. I don't like to be away from him. He's the love of my life. When we have time together, we just want to make the most of it. He makes me feel "all together." When we are apart I feel out of sorts. This is a blessing from God and I know this. I hope you find that soul that supports you, whether a partner or a friend. Don't be afraid to let that person in.

We love to cook. I'm his sous chef; he looks up recipes and we try them. When he's working on his art, I like to watch and talk about what he's doing. His art is different from mine. I'm all concerned with details and reality, while his "pouring" is about color and movement. In fact, one of my favorite pieces is "Ghost Horse" which we made together. I took one of his pours and painted an oil of a horse on top. It's ethereal. It's how I see myself. The cover of this book is a copy of the orginal painting. I hope you'll like it.

We like to go to movies and concerts, and we enjoy traveling together. For our anniversary, we usually go to Aruba for a week, although this year we'll be at a family wedding. His daughter chose our anniversary day for her wedding, and that will be a wonderful way to celebrate. Before I have my colostomy, we're making a trip to Denver and I'm really looking forward to that. We'll be seeing a couple of bands we like at Red Rocks, and there's a wellness center where we'll stay. All the food they serve is healthy food, and there's workout equipment in every room. We'll rent a car and tool around. Going on a trip like that will help me stay in the moment. I'm trying not to focus a whole lot on what's coming up, because ready or not, it's going to come. It's like people always ask, "Are you ready for Christmas?" But honestly, it doesn't matter if "I'm ready" or not. It will come and it will go.

One of the things that Chris has had to give up, as my "cancer friend," is some of his privacy. It's been uncomfortable for him to have people just stopping by to visit. But he's a trouper, and if it makes me happy, he's on board. Can you imagine your spouse's response when someone wants to clean their bathroom or wash their underwear? Now you get it.

It might sound surprising, but the quality of our marriage—which has always been good—has actually gotten better since my diagnosis. We feel closer and are more patient with each other. Chris sits through every chemo session with me, and we face many of my doctor appointments together. When he's at work, sometimes I ride shotgun and sleep in the car while he's at a job site or visiting a client. He schedules "dates" at home, and makes me home-cooked meals on the grill. We don't ever let ourselves forget that every moment is precious. The loss of our son and dad is a constant reminder of this.

Something that's been just exceptional is how he has helped me feel beautiful. When I come home at night and want to take my wig off, he shows me that he still finds me attractive. He gives me kisses and hugs, and he has the most heart-stopping wink! Those little moments are so important. They help give me the grace to keep going. It helps me feel better about myself when I go out in public, too.

It takes a lot of commitment to care for me the way Chris does. He puts me to bed when I need to rest, puts two blankets on me because I'm so cold all the time. He'll put an earbud in my ear and play me a song he's listening to. He learned how to put on my wigs—how to put on the wig band, how to place it four fingers up from my brow so the wig will be in the right place. He helps me do my nails and he puts my lashes on. That takes patience, and he's doing all this before he has to go to work himself! After I broke my shoulders and on days when I was really exhausted from treatments, he even gave me my morning shower and dried my hair.

When he does get to work, he's surrounded by his own set of "cancer caregiver friends." The guys at his company are always checking in about how I'm doing and how he's doing. They ask him what they can pray about, and then they follow up to find out what's happening. His best friend, John, has given a different kind of care. He'll call and say, "Let's just go fishing today." And having a friend who does that kind of regular, ordinary activity with him is really valuable. The kind of friends who can take care of the caregivers are so precious.

Feb. 23, 2023 Chris Starts My At-Home Chemo

Part of Chris' caregiving was to administer 22 days of at-home chemo after the infusion treatments ended. The guidelines around this are pretty scary. He had to wear gloves because it would be dangerous for him to have contact with the chemicals. We couldn't use the same restroom because it would be dangerous for him to encounter my waste. This is poison that he's giving me. And he did it for 22 days— more than three weeks. It went against all effort I had to be well. But I'm trusting God and the doctors He's given to me.

The way the doctors explain my treatment, the chemo and therapy will keep working for about six months after I've finished with it. The radiation works like a torch burning away the tumor. As the cancer is being radiated, it can shoot off little particles that could let it spread. So you take chemo along with it because the chemo kills anything that escapes the radiation. Then, as you're healing, your body forms scar tissue that closes off the areas that were hurt by the cancer or the treatments.

My doctors talk about my case every Wednesday in the hospital's tumor board. They're trying to learn from my experience, and I hope my experience proves to be a good lesson for them. Maybe they will decide to do the radiation and chemo combo first as it keeps circulating and then infusion after. That would be an unexpected legacy, to help them determine the best course for those who follow in my footsteps. It can be hard for me to wait for them to decide on the next steps. I have to trust God's timing and their expertise.

How Cancer Friends Communicate

Cancer friends might understand what's happening from their own experiences, or they might just pay close enough attention that they get it right. So they tend to ask things that are very specific, making it easy for you to say, "Yes!"

- "Could I come over tomorrow to do your laundry?"
- "When is a good time for me to come and wash your floors?"
- "Can I stop over Friday to clean your bathrooms?"
- "How about I bring lunch to your shop and sit with you in the break room for a bit?"

I'm living with a "chemo brain" and I'm not as able to think things through as usual. So it works really well if you don't need me to decide what you might do or figure out when our schedules will work.

Cancer friends also keep their radar up so they can recognize if somebody is asking for something without saying it out loud. When my friend Marcie was dying, she really wanted to get out, but she didn't want to go out looking the way she did. When she told me that the permanent makeup I'd done for her was making her more comfortable being seen, that cued me that she might like to borrow some of my wigs. I could offer what I could do because I was listening to her needs.

Cancer Friends Help!

A cancer friend also leaves the door open for you to make very specific requests. Some of what mine have heard from me include:

- Will you help me do my laundry? I can't hang these shirts with my broken shoulder. I'll make you some tea while you do my laundry.
- Would you call my clients to reschedule our appointments? It's

hard for me to have to explain my medical situations 30 times.

- I can't meet you for coffee, but could you sit with me and visit at my clinic between clients?

Other helpful things they've done include:

- Picking up my mail and bringing it to me.
- Sending thank you notes for me.
- Cleaning my bathrooms.
- Cleaning the floors.
- Hanging up the clean clothes (since I can't reach the high rack right now).
- Changing my bed linens. (This is a challenge for the little Italian T-Rex.)
- Bringing food.
- Emptying and loading the dishwasher.
- Taking the trash out.

Cancer is a good teacher if you're not very experienced in asking for the things you need or want. It also can help you understand some things about other people you might not have recognized at first. When I was taking care of my mother, she could get upset that my sisters who live in the area weren't stepping up to help. And I've certainly felt that way myself sometimes about some of the people I know. But I've learned to put myself in their position. They're busy, and dealing with my mortality reminds them of their own mortality. A lot of people just don't want to deal with that. When I got my diagnosis, I was already deep into my own confrontation with mortality. Besides, mom was happy if I came by on my lunch break and cuddled up next to her in the bed. Memories flood me of giving her showers and laughing at the huge bug in the corner. I didn't tell her was there until we were done! I still laugh at that.

How the Church Helped

Church isn't just a building where there are people you worship with. We felt so much encouragement from people just BEING the church. We got so much support from people we didn't even know, and not all of them were part of our congregation either.

Chris's company, Atlanta Flooring, does a lot of work for the builder True Homes, and they were a very consistent prayer partner for us. When he was on site, they would ask what's happening with me and they would stop and pray right there and then, from bosses to the crews who were working on tile and flooring. It's been like another family to us. Atlanta Flooring gave him time off whenever he needed it. That's how he was able to go with me to all my chemo appointments: they have been helpful in a real way. My friend Martha's Catholic church had a mass said for me. Another friend started a Vemno to help cover a $1,330 chemo copay, then my daughter organized a GoFundMe among her friends to help us out until I reached the deductible for the year. A friend who works in the insurance industry has been constantly helping me make phone calls to figure things out. I never would have asked for financial help.

Christian radio has been a real blessing to me. KLOVE radio will pray with me anytime. If you call or text, a real person will call you back and pray with you. Their music is uplifting and encourages me, and that's been a huge part of my healing. It helps me not to feel sorry for myself. People are out there that really care.

Then there are the ladies from my church who came over and helped me clean my house when I couldn't reach to clean with my shoulder being out of commission. Someone anonymously donated a cleaning service. They've brought us meals. My friend Melissa catered my Christmas open house at work just because they love us. I see Christ in their love.

"Oh that my words were written! Oh that they were recorded in a book!"

Job 19:23

FEELING LIKE JOB

My cancer diagnosis was the third strike against my life in just over 15 months. My stepson, Christopher, died in July 2021. He was only 24 years old. My father-in-law, who had been living with us for nine years, died on Sept. 26, 2022. Then I got my diagnosis not even two weeks later.

Nobody wants to be God's poster child for suffering. I cried endless tears and had entire months when I was early-to-bed because I just didn't have anything left in me. The darkness in my mind grew deeper as I grew weaker physically from the treatments. Grief for our son, our father, and my "old life" was very real and raw. Even writing this makes my throat tighten.

I was still trying to work full-time while, being realistic, I had to be thinking about my will and final planning in case things went badly. Well-intentioned loved ones and friends constantly wanted explanations about how I was doing. And I couldn't tell them: I wanted everything to just be over. I wasn't just grieving the loss of our son and father, I was grieving all my expectations for how life would be. I grieved for Chris, and how his life was so different than he expected it to be.

Why me? I would think. Then I'd ask myself, Why **not** me? But I'd never expected to have to put so much effort into things that nobody would really understand unless they'd been through it themselves.

May 10, 2023 The Story of Job ... again ... and again

About that time, the Bible story of Job came up three times for me: first in my daily devotional, then in our Bible study couples group, then I was in a radiation waiting room and heard Dr. David Jeremiah sharing about this.

That's not a Bible book I ever wanted to study, One thing after another happens to Job. Satan asks God if He "had considered His servant Job?" Then there's this weird interaction where Satan negotiates with God Himself. He says that Job only served God because God blesses him so much. Then God agrees to take his hand of blessing off Job's life ... and Satan can do anything but kill him. Betrayal flags are screaming in my brain. Job loses his children. He lost his career. He didn't know that later it would be restored. Job was mad at God and mad at his friends and he was telling God how mad he was.

I was feeling like he was! In the Psalms, it talks about how all of God's waves have gone over this person (Ps. 42:7, 88:7), and that's what it was like. You think you're done, you've come up and gotten your breath, then all of a sudden another big wave comes right at you and knocks you back down. In Psalm 88, it says, "You have afflicted me with all Your waves ... Your terrors have cut me off. They came around me all day long like water; They engulfed me altogether (v.7, 16-17). That's how it felt.

And unfortunately, there were also friends like Job's friends who showed up. There was one woman I remember—a very spiritual woman—and I was sharing a little with her about my struggles. She said, "But God promised in the Word your healing. Maybe you're not choosing to be healed."

Well, I believe God heals, and sometimes I feel betrayed that He hasn't healed me. But she just made me angry. Meaning well, she cut me deeper in the betrayal that lurked in my heart.

And then Job gets focused on who God is. He says, "I know that my redeemer lives." He thinks about his relationship with God, and he says "even after my skin has been destroyed, in my flesh I will see him." Job expected that one day, he would see God face to face, not as a stranger but as a friend, and he longed for that day: "I myself will see him with my own eyes—I and not another. How my heart yearns within me!" (Job 19:25-27, NIV) God will recognize me as His friend, not a stranger. Hallelujah!

It became really comforting to me to really understand that verse. He'd lost his health and his family and he knew he was still in relationship with God. It helped me to remember that even if my flesh is destroyed and I lose my beauty and everything physical I think is part of me, I'll still be whole. I'll be okay.

A friend once told me, "We are heavenly beings just here for a while having a human experience." This life is a short time, and my time with God is forever.

Mother's Day 2023: A Trip to the ER

Mother's Day wasn't what I'd hoped for. Everybody was busy with their own families, of course, but my daughter sent me a flower bulb to plant. I couldn't have enjoyed spending time with them anyway because I was throwing up nonstop. My stomach hurt, all the time; I couldn't eat or drink. It had been going on long enough that I had lost a lot of weight, and things just weren't getting any better. The doctors had found a blocked liver bile duct and at first they hoped it would resolve on its own. They said the problem usually resolves when the chemo and radiation treatments stop. No such luck. I was septic and felt like I wouldn't make it another day.

So Chris took me to the emergency department on Mother's Day, and I was in the hospital for a whole week. I really don't have any memories from that time. I know they put in a stent, and I know that this kind of stone can be related to both the cancer and the treatments. But I was too sick to really remember anything that happened. I do remember after surgery having accidents in the bed; and the kind doctors and nurses who cleaned me up. I was apologizing up and down and my female doctor put on gloves and a hazmat suit and took care of me. She said she didn't get to be a doctor by not doing stuff like this. What grace she extended to me! My dignity went out the window and sometimes I wonder if I'll ever get it back.

June 20, 2023 Hope Revived!

On Monday, they ran another MRI on me, and today they did another sigmoidoscopy. They didn't find anything! I'll know next week if they are okay going with a "watch and wait" approach or if they think I need more treatment. I tell my family and best friends and we rejoice.

The doctors are taking a cautious approach so I'm getting scanned again at the beginning of July. After that, I'll know what my next step is. It'll either be great news or it'll be a little disappointing. If I have to have my colon removed, then I'll have to wear an ostomy bag, and that's another hit to my physical body that I don't want to face.

In the work I do, I have to be very careful because what I do is permanent on somebody's body. Yes, you can fix things that someone else has done wrong, and I do a lot of repair work on bad permanent makeup that was maybe done by someone who is just learning this profession. But things can be hard to fix. There's a lot of risk, and you have to be confident in the person who's working on you. Wearing an ostomy bag might make my clients think I'm not well. I wonder how I will hide this from them. Will I even need to?

I'm a doer. I don't like idle time. I feel like time is precious and you have to maximize your time. Those downtimes, waiting times … I know God is in the waiting and I don't have to be doing something profound all the time. Still, I want to be the best at what I do. I want a clean house. I want my projects finished. I want my paintings done.

But why? Really why? There needs to be a balance here. And that means sometimes I need other people not to rush in to help or grab my downtime for a visit. Sometimes I need other people to just breathe with me, and give me space to learn. Why do I have to push myself when I don't expect the same from my clients or my family?

My husband and I are really good at walking together. We walk together in honesty, and we let each other know that this is the moment you have and you need to be honest through it. There's a lady I talk with often at church and she's like that, too. She will sit with me and cry with me and not tell me I have to do one thing or another.

July 8, 2023: Another Blow

The news today was not good news. The doctors say they have to cut away part of my colon and set me up with an ostomy bag. That was a bit of a setback. You think things are fine, then the cancer rears its head again.

This is another hit to my self-esteem. I feel mad. I feel gross. It's summer and I don't know if I want to be in a bathing suit. Will I want to travel when I'm not sure how to take care of something that's new to me? Am I going to lose my practice?

"At least you'll have your life," the doctors say. "You can't do anything if you're dead."

Well, yes, that's true. My friend Marci just died from her cancer. And that was her choice. She wanted to spend the end of her life with her family, doing things she wanted to do, not in treatment. I have to respect that. But I have to get back to work! Putting the brakes on my career could force a whole new chapter in my life. "I might lose my business, but I'll have my life," they say. Right now, I'm not really at ease with that idea, and I feel those words as hammers on my head. I feel like a crybaby facing this, and they are probably thinking I'm the worst primadonna.

The doctor didn't even give us the option to watch and wait. They told me that if this particular area showed cancer regrowth later, they wouldn't be able to do anything about it. They said they may be able to reverse the surgery in three to six months when they can see how well I've healed.

I went down a Google rabbit hole trying to find out what's really going on, because I am sure the doctors don't tell you everything up front. I'm not ready to give up! All I know is that I'm going to feel even less like my own self, when I'm trying to take care of an ostomy bag. I'll see an ostomy nurse in August to learn more about placement, supplies, and care. I learned I will spend a week in the hospital, then two more weeks off and I could go back to work. Since there's a private bathroom at my studio, I'm thinking I'll be able to take care of myself there.

Panic Attack!

I think we've already established that I like to keep a lot of balls in the air and I'm good at that. So on Wednesday, I was driving home from the clinic, which is just 10 minutes from our house. Chris was at the grocery store and he called me. I picked up—hands-free, of course!—and I was having some trouble hearing him. It sounded like the call was cutting in and out, so I started trying to fix my phone so I could hear him more clearly. It turned out later I was just hearing the voice of a lady from church who was talking to him while he was talking to me, but I didn't know that at the time. So I'm trying to talk with Chris and to fix my phone and to drive myself back home. There was a car behind me and I started to worry whether I was going too fast or slow. All of a sudden, my heart was racing and my hands were tingling. I was confused. I didn't know where I was. Had I made my turn or not? What road was I on? I broke into a cold sweat.

I managed to get home and ran upstairs to our room. I kept checking my Apple watch, and could see that my heart rate was going faster and faster. That made me even more upset. Chris came home and I told him, "I don't want to go to the ER!" So we called my nurse oncologist.

"I think you're having a panic attack," she said calmly. "I would have expected you to be having them now. With the news you just got, and all that you've been through, it's not surprising."

I told her I didn't want to go to the ER and she strongly agreed. "The ER will want to hold you and run tests. But you're in a compromised health situation. Your heart's not beating so hard it will stop. Just get into a quiet place and practice your breathing."

A 'Shitfest' Year: Feeling Old

I always thought getting old would be more of a process, but this year feels more like a cut-and-dried divide. This is the year of my life when my youth said goodbye and the older version of me said hello. Then I was young, now I'm older. It makes me feel like I'm giving up. But in another way, it's just being honest with myself.

Chris and I went out to dinner and a movie late one afternoon, and we looked around the restaurant and said to each other, "We're part of the old crowd now." Suddenly, I'm thinking that we'll be going to dinner parties where all the conversations are about medical treatments. And I don't want that!

My stepson's girlfriend, Lindsay, is so sweet and she has a lot of wisdom. She tells me, "You're so amazingly strong and resilient, you're going to get through this. Day to day, life goes on and nothing goes the way we want. But one day we're going to look back at 2023 and say, 'That was some shitfest that happened to you! What was all that crap? Do you remember that?'"

Honestly, I'm hoping I don't remember it! But she lightened the moment for sure. Of course, it wouldn't have sounded the same if we didn't love each other. When she tries to express her love like that, it's different than when someone you don't know well does it. Lindsay is someone I need. I need her love. I was so happy just having her be there. She needed to talk and I know that about her, so it was okay. But other people, I really need them to listen.

KEEPING THE HOUSE UP

Let me just start by saying: I'm not a princess who lives in a palace and always has other people do everything for me. I'm a businesswoman who lives in a regular house with my husband, Chris, our son, Dillon, and our two boxers, Hannah and Opie. I love to sit outside in the summer and enjoy the flowers my husband plants.

For about nine years now, we've lived in the little tiny farmhouse my mom left me when she passed. It was pretty small for us at first, especially since Chris' dad was still living with us at the time. Chris and I slept on the floor in the living room while Chris built an attached garage with a master suite above it. He is so creative and capable! Our bedroom has an amazing headboard he created using the front porch columns from an old house. He made a beautiful bookshelf out of salvaged copper pipe and live-edge boards. The wood wall in our living room is paneled with old wood from our barn. When my treatments made it hard for me to climb the stairs for a while, Chris redid the first floor bath and the bedroom where my Mom and his father had lived. So if I needed to stay downstairs I could.

Cleaning and organizing my home is something I've always enjoyed. That said, cancer got in the way of keeping up our home. I like to clean and I like things to be clean, but with cancer and then my shoulder injuries, I've had to let some of my own cleaning go. Like, I'm sitting here right now and I see dust on the hardwood floor under the dresser and it's going to stay there. Before, I would have moved everything out from under there and cleaned it immediately! Or maybe it would never even have gotten dusty, because before cancer, doing floors was an everyday thing for me. Some of the hardwood floors in this house are the original three-quarter inch red oak floors—they're just beautiful.

Decluttering has been a big thing. Chris and I are trying to simplify things. We're not keeping as many clothes, and we're trying not to hold onto every little thing. We're donating a lot of things or giving them away to people who will appreciate them. We're both working at finishing our unfinished projects, and we're not taking on so many new ones. And we're still dealing with our parents' stuff: in the barn there's a lot of my mother's stuff; we're still dealing with his father's stuff; and my mother-in-law, who helps me, also has a lot of stuff. We're very aware that if anything happens to us, Meghan and Dillon are not going to want to deal with all our stuff.

A weekly cleaning service is great if you can afford it. But they can't do everything for you. Friends are a great help when they offer to do some of the specific tasks that you can't do. These vary, depending on what's happening with you at any given time. At different times, some of the kinds of help that were most helpful to me included:

- Doing the laundry. This worked well when people would just carry my baskets of dirty clothing away and either do the loads at home or take them to the cleaners, then return everything clean and folded or on hangers. When I'm feeling up to it, I might have them run the loads at my house while we visit over a cup of tea.

- Clean my bathrooms.

- Dust my house.

- Change the bed and bath linens.

- Pick up my mail.

- Write and send thank you notes for me.

- Prepare food for me and my family members. Sometimes I'm not feeling well enough to eat, let alone cook, but everyone else is hungry!

- Empty and load the dishwasher.

- Take the trash out—from the house to the trash cans, and also from the garage to the street on trash day.

- Cut the grass.

- Walk the dogs.

It's a hard thing that you may find you need to enlist help, not just accept it. But the people who provide tangible help are also being blessed by the chance to do this little piece of God's work in this world. Learn to welcome their support, and know that God is using your current need to bless them.

Don't be concerned about the outward beauty of fancy hairstyles, expensive jewelry, or beautiful clothes. You should clothe yourselves instead with the beauty that comes from within, the unfading beauty of a gentle and quiet spirit, which is so precious to God.

1 Pet. 3:3-4 (NLT)

THE POSITIVE VALUE OF LEARNING A NEW WAY OF LIFE

Just before I found out I had cancer, Chris took me skydiving for my birthday. I wanted to go skydiving because a friend had done it, and it looked like something I could do, too.

It took about an hour and a half to drive to the airport in Raeford, this tiny little town in Hoke County. It's the county seat and there's less than 5,000 people who live there. The airport is tiny, too. It has just one runway, and it shares its hangar with a VFW post.

So the plane went up to 16,000 feet. We're all sitting in the back of the plane straddling this bench, and all of a sudden you see that there are people missing. It feels like they keep getting sucked out of the plane, and you're moving up closer to where they got sucked out.

If you've ever flown on a plane, you've gone up above the clouds. When you're skydiving, the clouds are a mist and you can feel yourself go through them. At one point, it's sunny and suddenly it's not because you're really moving very fast through the air. It was so disorienting for me … the air was roaring in my ears and the changing altitude messed with my ears.

Chris has jumped, and he's doing flips and stuff with his instructor. Me … no way! Even though I was only freefalling for about 30 seconds, it felt like a long time. The instructor is saying look over here, look over there, and I'm thinking, "No! I only want to land!"

It was interesting up there when I pulled the chute—how quiet it was all of a sudden. You're hearing the wind when you're freefalling, but once your chute is up you don't hear the wind rushing or anything. It's totally different up there than down here. You look off at the horizon and you can see that the horizon is curved. Amazing to see a new perspective. Is that how God sees my life?

When I landed, Chris asked, "Why are you talking funny? Why are you holding your mouth like that?" Apparently, the left side of my mouth was kind of droopy. It turns out that I'd suddenly developed Bell's Palsy, which can happen when you experience a sudden shock or trauma. When I watch the video of my skydive, I can see it start when they're talking to me on the plane before I jump. We went to the doctor, and he gave me a shot of steroids which helped. The palsy started again when I began chemo, so I guess that's my body saying "This is another big shock."

I still can't believe I went skydiving. I'm glad I did it, although I don't think I'll do it again. Maybe that's how I will feel about cancer. I don't think I'll do it again …

Thinking Differently

Cancer changes your way of thinking. I think differently now. I'm thinking more with eternity in mind. I've also really simplified my life. I've made my routine simpler and less stressful. I'm trying not to totally cram my schedule at work, but let myself know when I need an hour between clients. Some days I feel like Jello, like I might cry at any minute. I never know whether today is going to be one of those days. I can't be pushing at things when my body, or my heart, or my emotions might need rest.

It's nice not to put so many things in your day! Chris has been making nice simple suppers for us—maybe grilling bite-size pieces of salmon or something like that. I just want to hang out with him and enjoy ourselves.

Listening Well

As I've discovered how much I want people to just listen to me, I've learned that it can also be nice just to listen to other people and not have to talk about myself. I've always had compassion on my mastectomy patients, but now I bring to the listening an awareness of what they've been through. I don't have to say what's happened to me. The change is inside.

I listen more when women come to me for help buying wigs because they're losing their hair from chemo. I've learned to listen without having my reply already cocked. One lady was telling me that she'd just moved here from another state and her oncologist here wants to be very aggressive in treatment. She didn't even know her cancer was in Stage 3! It felt like her old doctor hadn't even told her. I just listened to her and prayed with her about what she's going to face. Maybe you'll think it's surprising, but I find those visits uplifting. They don't make me sad. They solidify the fact that I am there in their lives for a reason.

Speaking Without Words

There's this one couple, John and Melissa, who are our best friends. John does flooring and Chris supervises flooring installations, so they're in the same business. Melissa has been in the restaurant business forever and she's a great cook. We call their house "Coyle's Restaurant," and we get to eat there a lot! Those meals can turn into extended visits, and that's okay if you've had an extended visit relationship before cancer. You know each other and you don't have to talk about everything. Sometimes they come over to our house and we just sit outside and watch people parasailing from motorcycles near our house. They take off from a big field nearby and sometimes there's as many as five or six swooping over us and waving while we're out there. That's the beauty of just "Being." I want heaven to be like this.

Melissa gave me a bracelet that's really cool. It's just tiny beads on a rope bracelet, and it uses long and short beads to spell out "Be Brave" in Morse code. I love it! And that's an example of one way that a close friend can speak to you without words. Especially among close friends, no words are really needed. What a gift friendship is!

Letting Flexibility and Patience Take Root

Cancer has demanded that I become more patient and flexible. That's a bit ironic, because I'm having to be more flexible as my body has become less flexible. My shoulders are still painful, and it's easy to be upset with myself that I had this accident. It makes such a difference in your life when your arms don't work right! Physical therapy is painful and frustrating. I just have to go slow, don't push too far, and do what they say. This little T-Rex is becoming feisty!

I'm excited today because I'm drinking my soda water and I can hold my arm like a normal person. I'm not having to move my head funny to reach the straw. I've been using my limited range of motion to the max at work. I have good motion from my elbow down, so since I lay my patients way flat in the chair I'm able to work with them.

Meals … Well, I've never been a graceful eater. I'm Italian, what can I say? You're not Italian unless you've got sauce on your shirt! Chris helps me cut things up, but we're still always wiping dressing out of my hair. We can laugh about it now.

I'm also learning patience and flexibility with the people around me. I'm learning to let them "be" and not to expect them to meet my expectations. I'm developing a calmer mindset that's more ready to experience life as it comes instead of controlling.

Allowing Compassion to Grow

Cancer has forced me to become more compassionate, both toward others and toward myself. It's given me an uber-awareness of others whose lives are also challenging. Of course, the more empathetic and perceptive I become, the more aware I am when people are just blowing smoke! I'm much more aware of others in their suffering and also in their nonsense. I've learned when to take the back seat.

When you have to pay attention to suffering, you see your family and friends differently. You find opportunities to become more connected to people who are more understanding of what you're feeling, at the same time you become more understanding of what others are feeling. Your role in your family can change, because you aren't able to take charge in the same ways. Sometimes your friendships change also. It's all part of the new perspective you find in the value of life itself. You value life in a way you never did before.

Enjoying the Freshness of New Ways

I started wearing wigs back in February, when my top had thinned so much and I lost my widow's peak and hairline. For a while, I was just obsessed with hiding my thinning head of hair. I know my hair will grow back, but it won't grow back long! My hair's already starting to come in, but I'm going to have a new look, so that will bring a kind of freshness to my life. Maybe I look better without long hair pulling my face down? Would I have ever made this change in hairstyles if cancer had not dictated it?

I got my first wig from the lady who did my hair. She ordered me one that looked exactly like my own hair, then got me another one to wear when I wash the other. After that, I started experimenting. Wigs were like shoes to me. (It's taboo to ask me how many shoes I have and now, how many wigs do I have!) I mostly stayed with my own hair tone, but I tried some darker ones and a bright red one, too.

If you want to have hair and you have to wear wigs, have some fun with it! I named my wigs. The red one was Amy, because I felt like I looked like Amy Adams. Gayle was shorter and had a little more pouffiness than I'm used to—that's my real first name, my mom's name was Gayle. I even bought some wigs you can swim in.

I've found some new ways of thinking to bring to my clients also, as I have let them "in" to my challenge and discovered they are walking alongside me. In art classes, I'm looking for opportunities to broaden my student's thoughts and work and abilities.

After chemo ended, I was glad to enjoy the taste of food again! I've been discovering new flavors as well as going back to my favorites. I was a salty snack lover before—my dad was an engineer in a potato chip factory—but chemo made salt taste like acid. So I've discovered sweets. When I have more energy I'd love to cook more.

July 26, 2023 Buying Headstones

Today, we went to purchase headstones for our son Christopher and our dad. That was very hard. Christopher's been gone for two years already. Time has gotten away from us. I had to stop and remember how old he'd be today. He'd be 27! He was in a good place before he died, and we've had to spend a lot of time dealing with the grief of losing him.

Time feels like a vacuum, an empty space. You know how it is when you get an ear infection, and your ears just start to buzz? You think everyone else can hear it and it's hard to focus on anything else. Grief has come at us in waves. There are times when you just can't get your mind off stuff like that. It ebbs and flows. Throat dryness and tightening and then having to go on with everyday life. Appreciating those God has in your life at just the right times.

Narrowing focus, Enlarging Goals

When you have cancer, your goals change. My goals got bigger. Your priorities change when you're trying to maximize your energy and your time. I've said "Not right now" to a lot of projects lately. I won't be traveling for a while.

Someone wrote on Verywell Health, "Cancer isn't a sprint, it's a marathon—but the marathon doesn't have a finish line." That really is what it's like.

Life with cancer can be overwhelming for many reasons. You're trying to keep up with so many appointments—the oncologist, the radiologist, the surgeon. You're trying to work full-time. You're trying to figure out how you'll drive to appointments when you might not be in good condition to drive home afterward. You're trying to educate yourself. And my oncologist ordered me not to trust Dr. Google ... well, damn ... my search history speaks for itself.

I can't do all the things I used to do, so that makes my focus narrower. The latest activity I've had to release is my involvement with the Chambers of Commerce. I'm still a member, but I've stopped going to their meet and greets. I was supposed to host one, and I just can't. Business networking stretches me instead of supporting me. I used to go up to Orange County twice a year to support clients there—no more.

We're living in such an unbelievable time. The film industry can use artificial intelligence to make Harrison Ford look young again in a movie. People are enhancing their virtual appearance for online dating. And then, in some parts of the world, people have work done on their young children so it will be easier to arrange a good marriage for them. They have their child's jaw broken and their eyelids realigned. It can backfire, though, because then people want to know the medical history of the person they might marry. They want to make sure they won't have ugly children. How can the human race be that shallow? Ugly children. Maybe I need to reorient my focus …

But as cancer empties my life of some of these kinds of things, there's more room for God to create in me the kind of beauty that only God can create. The fruit of the spirit—peace, joy, forgiveness, longsuffering—we can't make those things happen by ourselves. They have to come from God. In this time of my life, I've been able to make room for God to grow some of those things in me. I hope when I get to my end, I'm Holy Spirit beautiful, not Hollywood good-looking.

Living with an Uncertain Future

Cancer is also overwhelming because the future becomes so uncertain. Living with cancer is really scary. It's important not to downplay that, or to sugarcoat what someone is dealing with. I wish my family and friends understood that—not that they could do anything about it.

It's a lonely thing, cancer is. Even with people surrounding you, you can get stuck in your head. Others can't really see or feel that for you. It's not their fault. It's a journey we take ourselves. It happens in your own head and body and there really are no words.

Facing off some kind of enemy is not an uncommon experience. Everybody's got something that they've survived. Everyone has their giants they've faced. They've survived it, and that's their story. But we hold people isolated in those stories. We expect them to get through alone living with those kinds of threats. When we pay more attention to these situations, we can step in and be present with them.

At this point in my experience, I know they plan to take the colon out, and I also know that's not the end. They're going to want to keep seeing me and keep scanning me and they'll keep asking, "How's she healing? Is there one more thing we need to do?" There's always the threat that you're not over it yet, which means there's always more exams and treatments. It's not at all the kind of life I expected at age 57.

Being honest with myself, I have limitations with my shoulder now, and with my diet and bathroom routines. I'm going to have to learn to care for the ostomy and how to plan my day, work, and home around that. It means I'll be saying no to things that will drain me, mentally and physically.

It also means genuinely planning the end-of-life stuff. Preparing for the end of life doesn't sound positive, but tying up those loose ends can give you a lot of contentment. Wills, plots, wishes … when those are in place, you feel more ready. You secure a place to put your remains; you leave a legacy … not just stuff. That's one of the reasons I'm writing this book. Maybe it will help you as you walk your own journey. Maybe it can help your loved ones help you while you travel that road.

The reality is: Everyone's going to die. Your positive thinking isn't going to make you live any longer. When the end comes, you want to be ready. You talk to God more, and listen to His voice, and you embrace what Jesus did for you … and you know you'll live forevermore … maybe soon. You'll be Ethereal and Eternal.

An honest answer is like a kiss on the lips.

Prov. 24:26 (NIV)

FIVE PRACTICAL SELF-CARE TIPS FOR THE SUPERHUMAN WOMAN

When you are in treatment for cancer or another serious illness, the things you usually think of as "self-care" aren't always possible. But you can make sure yourself is cared for by letting others take care of what's most important to you.

My husband, Chris, has been remarkable. Remember, he works in the construction industry. Helping a woman look beautiful isn't one of his regular skills. (Although I have to tell you: He's really good at helping this woman feel beautiful, and that makes a huge difference, especially now!)

So a lot of the "self care" he did for me was helping me with my routines. He learned how to put on my wig band so it set in the right place, four fingers above my brows, and he learned to put my wigs on. He would do my brows and eyelashes. I'd lay down on the bed and he'd position himself above me with his phone's flashlight for extra illumination, lash glue, and strip lashes. He did my nails for me. Nails are important to me because even if you're in bed all day, your hands are always in front of you! It made me smile that he would always put on Dean Martin radio and call it his "beauty routine soundtrack." Then I still give myself a facial every Wednesday and spray tan my face and neck for a "self-glow," so I won't need a base makeup.

Not everyone understands why it's important to me to look good even while I'm in treatment, but it is important to me, so that makes it part of my essential self-care.

I think I'm like lots of women: I like to keep everything going for everyone around me. Cancer definitely challenges that "superwoman" way of life. As a result, I've learned several new ways of caring for myself that fit the life I'm really living right now. Here are five self-care essentials I've learned during this difficult time.

1. *Hang onto your sense of perspective.*

This life isn't our end goal. As someone has said, "We are heavenly beings having an earthly experience." You have to look at this life with that point of view. This life is the canvas we're painting, and you have to keep the canvas in front of you and do the best painting you can. But this life won't last forever. And when it seems like life is just going up in flames, it's good to remember that you can't paint roses on a burning canvas. Do what you can with what you have, and leave the rest to God.

2. *Be honest with God.*

You really can't bargain with God, but you have to talk with him. About everything. I remember knowing that God could just heal me, then facing a feeling of betrayal because he could do it and he hadn't. So, I thought, he must not want to heal me, and did that mean he doesn't love me? I mean, if he loved me, why wouldn't he want to heal me? That could turn into a real rabbit hole if I just stayed in my own head. But when I spoke honestly with God about what I was feeling, it opened me up to receiving emotional healing from Him. At the same time, I know that my feelings right now can change a lot, even from moment to moment, just because my body is under so much stress. I can cry at the drop of a gnat, but is it profitable for me at the time? There's times to be emotional, and there's times to pull up your big girl panties and walk on. I have to deal with my emotions the same way I would clean out my closet. You have to sort through which things go to Goodwill, which things go in the trash can, and which things you want to hold onto.

3. *Be honest with yourself.*

You can't just go and put everything back the way it was before your diagnosis. I like Danny Gokey's song, "Tell your heart to beat again, Yesterday's a closing door. You don't live there anymore." Knowing that things have changed and you can't ever go back is a major hit to your gut, but being honest with yourself can help you walk through a new door. There are going to be days when you won't want to get out of bed, and days when you're not able to get out of bed. Give your body and mind grace, and let yourself know that that's okay.

Cancer means accepting limits. Your time for other things is limited because so much time goes to appointments and treatments. Your energy is limited, both because of the cancer and because of how the treatments affect you. You have to be honest with yourself that this is a time when you have to live within those limits. I can't run a 5K right now. Maybe I will later, I can't reach the top of my head with the blow dryer ... maybe I will later.

4. *Be honest with your people and your loved ones.*

I really need to be honest with the people who matter most to me. If I'm scared or overwhelmed it's okay to share that, even if some people I thought were close just don't want to deal with it. You also need to let people understand that a visitor can be exhausting! It's great when people just drop by for a few minutes to say hello, maybe drop off food, but not stay long. You can give them a little update but they don't need your whole medical history. When I was first diagnosed, a lot of people were bringing meals over. Those meal trains are awesome, but people forget you're still going through stuff. We ended up freezing a lot of them for later. And then there's the point that everyone else's life just goes on and you're still feeling "stuck."

The people who need your honesty include your employer. In my business, every client is my employer, so I have to keep them in the loop about what's going on. They need to know things like "I'm getting surgery on this day and I'll be out of the office for a week." Chris has to keep his employer informed, too. They've been really good about giving him time off when he wants to be at the doctor with me.

5. *Talk with others who've worked through the same hard stuff.*

I have counsel and sound wisdom, I have insight, I have strength. (Prov. 8:14, RSV)

The cancer center I was part of had a lady call me who'd been through the same treatment. Every time I started a new thing she would give me some perspective—real practical conversations so I would know what to expect. Be open to listening, because these are people who can have wisdom for you. Keep your radar up for people who are attuned to you. These will not be people who claim to have answers; they will be those who show up for you. They may seem silent but it's because they're attentive and listening to you. They'll take time to tell you their story someday. But their story will be a secondary thing … first, they want to hear yours.

A Few More Tips: Scents and Shopping

Part of being in treatment involves choosing a new way of shopping. You'll want to try new styles in clothing that work for what you're doing now. It's a new era of scarves, and lots of pretty draping is available. I've come to like the Boho trend. But shopping in stores is going to be overwhelming and exhausting. I used to like to shop, but I just don't have the energy to walk around and check out everything that might work for me. Shop online. I was in the middle of chemo as Christmas approached, and I did all my holiday gift shopping for the grandkids online. That made for some big package deliveries, but it was very helpful to me at the time.

Being able to smell a pleasant aroma really helps me. Not food smells, but clean, fresh scents. I use essential oils, candles, and wax cubes to put the scents I enjoy around me.

Just Being Honest with You

You can tell that honesty is a big part of what self care during cancer looks like for me. Looking honestly at the things cancer has been teaching me can be hard.

Aug. 10, 2023 A Sobering Encounter

We have a friend whose husband just died, and they were close like Chris and me. I can't imagine what she is dealing with. I don't think I could cope. I don't want to die and leave Chris to cope either. We're still both dealing with the death of his son, my stepson Christopher, and that's two years ago. It's been an ongoing grief for us both.

There's a scripture that describes what it is like when God strips all the idols away from His chosen people, Israel. God compares his people to a prideful woman whose life is focused on flirting with men, gaining their attention with her beautiful clothes and jewelry. He says he will "strip away everything that makes her beautiful: ornaments, headbands … earrings, bracelets and veils; scarves … perfumes and charms; rings, jewels, party clothes, gowns, capes, and purses" and much more (Isa. 3:18-23). Isaiah concludes the prophecy:

Instead of smelling of sweet perfume, she will stink. She will wear a rope for a sash, and her elegant hair will fall out. She will wear rough burlap instead of rich robes. Shame will replace her beauty. (Isa. 3:24, NLT)

This is how I felt: I felt a lot shame as cancer eroded some of my own physical beauty. But that's not how God sees me. He's looking at my inside. Which is why I don't want to die ugly.

A HOPE AND A FUTURE

I am writing this book from in the middle of my cancer treatment journey. I've had months of chemo and radiation. The most recent tests showed that the treatments had not reduced the cancer enough. I'm scheduled for colostomy surgery at the end of the month. At this point in treatment, it's pretty easy to feel low. And part of what I'm doing by writing this book is reminding myself that what I'm experiencing today is not what I'll experience forever. God promises "hope and a future" to all of His children (Jer. 29:11) and I am looking forward to the future—not just my eternal future with God, but the day much sooner when I'll see this book published.

The Hopes I'm Releasing

This moment is one where I really have to hold onto hope intentionally. Cancer takes so many things away from your life. Getting ready for a cancer surgery isn't like going to get a plastic surgery job, that adds something to yourself. This just keeps taking things from me. There are positive things that happen, true; but it also takes a lot from you. Cancer takes time, energy, and your sense of certainty. It takes what you thought was a normal life schedule. Like–I don't want to go to the movies at 7:30 anymore, I want to be in bed! Cancer takes some of your priorities away. I would usually be thinking ahead to the Christmas open house at work, but right now I'm just waiting to see how I'll feel. It takes some of your friendships. And to be honest, those are probably relationships you needed out of your field of stress anyway! You get less interested in the kind of frivolous friendships where you can't tell them you've been picking out your headstone. (I haven't chosen mine yet, but it's a good example.)

As you live through your own struggle—whether with cancer or something else—what do you know that you can look forward to? We know that we can look forward to the beautiful future that God describes in the Bible, when "He will wipe every tear from their eyes, and there will be no more death or sorrow or crying or pain" (Rev. 21:4). At that wonderful time, we will be living in a place where tears don't exist any more.

The Hopes I Am Holding

"For I know the plans I have for you," declares the Lord, *"plans to prosper you and not to harm you, plans to give you hope and a future.* (Jer. 29:11, NIV)

In this life, our hopes are less glorious but no less important to us. So part of the journey with cancer or any serious illness is to give yourself things to look forward to. When you watch older people, you notice that they often choose to pass right after a holiday or a birthday, something they were looking forward to. It's important to give yourself things to look forward to. Some of those are big and some are small, but they're all part of living the future and hope that God has given now.

So next week I'm having dinner with a friend who's going to make us salmon. Thursday night, we're going to the movies. In the beginning of August, we're going to Denver for a week. We'll see a couple of concerts at Red Rocks and just tool around. I'm going to focus on being there and enjoying my time.

My big goal is to rent a house in Aruba for a whole month when this is over with. I've been working on a painting of a carousel horse, not a commission for somebody else but just a painting that I can take time with and enjoy being in the process. When that painting, "Calliope," is done, I'll start another.

Resting in the Cancer Cocoon

Cancer has become something of a cocoon for me. It's a time that I'm being forced to rest, to wait, and to let changes happen to me instead of planning how the changes would happen.

I liked my life the way it was. I had my jobs, my career, my hair, my health, my husband, and my grandchildren. I was like that caterpillar that's just as happy as can be eating her leaves. And then all of a sudden, there's new work going on inside a cocoon.

A lot of waiting happens in my cocoon. It's a form of isolation, and in some ways you might not think it's good to be isolated. But when you're sad and terrified, it's best to be quiet. When I go into my room and lie down on my bed, it feels safe. I do a lot of praying there.

When I homeschooled Meghan, we brought cocoons indoors and raised them until the butterflies came out. One thing I learned from that: you can't rush that process! There's important stuff happening in that waiting time. There's more to that transformation than I knew.

First, caterpillars need a different food than butterflies. You give them leaves when they're caterpillars, then you put sugar water on little pads for them to drink when they come out as butterflies, before you release them.

Caterpillars can't see clearly. They have a very simple eye, and rely more on their sense of touch. They feel vibrations that alert them to what's going on around them. A butterfly has two large eyes that can detect color. That helps them recognize the flowers where they can get nectar.

Because of how they're made, a caterpillar has very simple goals. A caterpillar wants to eat, to hide on a leaf, to be camouflaged from predators. Then it makes a cocoon, and the caterpillar has no clue what's going to happen. It just knows it's time to build the cocoon. When they turn into a butterfly, their life is completely different. They don't blend in anymore. They appreciate color and the flight of life after they've earned their wings.

Cancer is like being in that cocoon. Everything is changing, and I don't have the big picture. All I can do is wait to see what will happen.

At the same time, I know that there is a Master Artist who has the big picture in view. It's kind of like when Chris was remodeling the house. He had a vision for the house that I couldn't understand. He would show me the blueprints and explain to me where things were going, but until I saw the walls go up I was lost. God has a vision for each of us that we may not understand until the "walls" are formed.

I also think that, from God's perspective, my time in the cocoon is a lot like that point in a portrait when I can see in my mind what it's going to look like, but the unfinished work in front of me doesn't make sense to anyone else. It's also like that waiting time when I'm working in oils. I have a vision of what I want to make, but with oils you have to let one layer dry before you can put the next layer on. You can't finalize details even if you have them in your head, because you have to wait for the earlier layers to dry. When I'm painting, that process can be exciting. I'm the kind of person who thinks about things when I'm laying in bed and can see the next thing that's coming. With painting, it's easier to trust the process and be excited about the next step.

With cancer, I haven't been feeling excited about what's coming. I feel more like that caterpillar with its very simple eyes that's gone into its cocoon. I know I'm going to get new cells. I might look different than I thought I would at the beginning. The change will come, and it will be whatever it is. But it'll still be me, and it'll be okay.

When you have a serious illness like cancer, only you know when it's safe to exit that cocoon. You'll know when it's right to take that next step. There are going to be days when you'll just want to go to bed and stay in bed. A lot of self-help books say you should get out of your head and push through, maybe go for a walk or do some other positive thing. A lot of friends can be the same way! My oncologist, on the other hand, told me I shouldn't push myself. "You're going through chemotherapy!" he said. "If you want to sleep, you should sleep." I was grateful for that.

So my bed became like my cocoon. During chemo, there were a lot of days when I went upstairs at 7 p.m. If we had company and I was still downstairs at 7:30, I was fighting back tears because I was so tired.

Sometimes people want to know more about what's happening than I'm ready to tell them. So right now, I'm not wanting to tell people I have bad news from my MRI. I know it's part of the process, but I don't want people to see that part. So I go into my cocoon. And like that caterpillar, I have no clue what's on the other side. I just know it's time to build the cocoon.

It reminds me of when I do people's portraits. There's a point in any portrait where I really don't want people to watch what I'm doing. I'm building the map, the structure of the face, the shadows, and I have a vision of what's coming but they can't see it. That likeness doesn't really happen until after I've done some really intense shading and other work. Then, all of a sudden, there they are on the canvas! "Ahhhh," they murmur. They see it! That's when I'm ready for them to look. I want them to wait until the picture will make sense to them.

And that's what my cocoon is for me: a place to wait until the picture makes sense. I hope that my experience will be something that can help other people. I know that if I'd had a "me" to tell me things to do, that would have been helpful. People like to know what is the next step so they can do it. It really helps when there's someone who can sense that it's the moment to recognize a "next step" coming, and who can help you say, "Wow! OK!" when the finished work is different than you expected.

Part of life in the cocoon is learning to accept things that aren't how I want them. I'm learning to love people where they are instead of making everyone my project. I'm not all the way out of the cocoon yet, but things seem to be happening even during my waiting time. Cancer is helping me understand what it means to live beautifully inside. Nobody can make fun of someone who lives with dignity and courage, accepting the things that come with honesty and grace.

The Hope that is Certain

And we believers also groan, even though we have the Holy Spirit within us as a foretaste of future glory, for we long for our bodies to be released from sin and suffering. We, too, wait with eager hope for the day when God will give us our full rights as his adopted children, including the new bodies he has promised us. (Rom. 8:23, NLT)

My career in beauty has given me the chance to meet so many amazing people who are finding their own beauty during very difficult times in life. One of my past clients was a young woman with alopecia, a kind of hair loss that can affect the hair all over your body. Science still doesn't know why it happens. And I helped this woman with eyebrows, but she went on to become a bald pageant queen. She chose to be beautiful within the limits of her own health set.

I've also had to learn to organize my life around some limits I never expected. So I prioritize which kind of client I'm going to see first thing in the morning when my body is the freshest and things don't hurt as bad. I save consultations for Friday afternoon when I'm physically spent. At this point, I have a pretty good sense of how I'm going to feel at different times, and I also know I'm going to have to figure this out all over again after my next surgery with my colon.

I'm looking forward to there being an end to all of this. I also know that the end might be when I'm called home. I used to want to be beautiful on the outside. Now I want to be beautiful on the inside because when the end comes, I know God is looking at the heart. And I want to die beautiful.

Open Your Heart To Those In Need

St. Jude Children's®
Research Hospital

American
Cancer
Society®

Made in the USA
Middletown, DE
06 April 2024